That's the title of the painting — And what would you call it?

....

Arearea

Gauguin

On the island of Tahiti...
I paint what I see. Look at these women
in their traditional Tahitian dresses. They're
dancing in front of a Tahitian idol.

**In Tahiti I paint...
the way I want to !**
That's why I left Europe.
It's all explained in my diary.
If you'd like, you can read it!

Do you like puzzles?
Then you'll like my painting! Each individual detail
was painted with a single color: the dog, orange;
the traditional Tahitian dress, white; the prairie,
green... Put all these pieces together and you've
got the pieces to a puzzle. If you don't believe
me, look at another painting... And so?

**I even wrote
in Tahitian on my painting!**
It's the title! The word means:
"Entertainment." Let me explain.
The girl in blue is playing a divo.
Another word you don't know? No
surprise, it's a Tahitian reed pipe!

What would you put on her traditional Tahitian dress... flowers or a plaid pattern?

FAUX

Faux ?
This stamp means "fake" in English.

The forger got all twisted around. He added 3 things that don't belong? Which painting were they taken from?

GAUGUIN

ARCAREA

PAR AVION
VIA AIR MAIL

Did Gauguin take a plane to go to Tahiti?
His plane ticket was discovered at an antique dealer.

☐ **True**

☐ **False**

15,718 kilometers...
that'll wear our your shoes (lyrics from a French song) That's the distance between Paris and Papeete. As for Gauguin it took him more than two months to reach Papeete!

Van Gogh

I've come to Arles for the sun
*My palette has changed. I use more lively colors.
Look how I play with shade and light.*

I finished this painting in January
*And yet harvest is in the summer! No, I didn't
fall on my head... I'm just paying a visit to
an asylum. I'm not allowed to leave and
I don't have any models. So, I paint
landscapes from my window or
I copy engravings, like this one.*

MILLET
Engraving

My friend Gauguin has left me
*He came to visit me in Arles.
We painted together.
It was great! And then
we had an argument...
So, I cut off an ear and
painted my portrait.*

They aren't the only ones!
There's also a sleeping couple on
another page. Who is it about?

....

The Sieste

A wagon
is also on another
page. Which?

....

Matisse

I paint with pure colors and thick strokes, I spread over the canvas
These colored areas could be a wall, a table or even a goldfish! Thus everything is simplified, including the perspective.

5th floor view on the Seine...
This my studio window. From it you see a landscape, a Parisian quay... and a still-life as well... with some very lively fish!

I "draw" with sheets of colored paper that I have cut!
Before gluing them, I pin them on a wall to see how they will look. You should try that. A lot of artists have!

Picasso and me
It's a long story. "We are as different as the north and south poles." But we greatly appreciate each other, even if our personalities are opposed!

What do you see
from the window?

....

Who painted these landscapes?

.... *Your turn...*

Picasso

Let me introduce you to my son
He's three years-old. This time I've dressed him up as a Harlequin. He's balanced on the edge of his chair. By now, he should be tired of posing! Surely, he would prefer to have fun with the toys I've made him...

Is this painting finished?
You bet it is! I've used three techniques: paint for the face and hands, for the feet, a drawing and you might say that I designed the costume from pieces of paper I cut out, then glued together. Doesn't that remind you of someone?

I love the circus
I've often used acrobats, jugglers and "pierrots", a French pantomime character... as models. It also seems that I dress like a clown!

I am also a sculptor
"You only need to cut up a painting to turn it into sculpture."

placement

Paulo, Picasso's Son, as Harlequin

...and not only him, I've also painted myself as a clown on canvas.

Who does this goblet belong to?

Oh, so so many hands! Who painted them?

The forger, caught with his hand in the purse!

Put yours on the page and trace its contour. Color it in and while you're at it, why not add a ring? For example, Modigliani's!

6 c
lec
der
pro
ren
che
nor
ter
ren
vez
ave
ran
il re
p
men
mie

Le
s'a

RK,
O

Put your finger print in the center of the magnifying glass

Why this title?
After all it's a painting of my friends.
And what would you call it?
....

The Balcony

I was inspired by this balcony. Mine is more modern.

GOYA

Manet

Our group often meets at my studio or in a café. There's Renoir, Monet, Bazille... We've all painted numerous canvases representing our period. Now, we want to paint our impressions. And it's just too bad if some people don't like it!

Here's Morisot I should say Berth... because it's a woman! She's a painter, a rare thing for a woman. We met at the Louvre. She's beautiful and she's talented. I've painted her portrait several times... She's married to my brother!

What's this scene about! Antoine is also a painter. How can he be smoking in a picture? That just isn't done! Fanny usually plays the violin with my wife. How strange that she's put on her gloves to go out on the balcony! Moreover, why is everyone looking her way?

Other friends ("people") of mine include Zola the writer, Baudelaire the poet, Nadar the photographer...

While cleaning the painting's background, the forger has revealed Léon's face to us. But... Who are the other three?

The mystery of the hidden son: Manet has painted 4 figures behind the balcony. It seems that Léon is his own son! Here, he's 17. But at 8 he had already posed for his father, who he called:

- [ ] **Daddy**
- [ ] **Godfather**
- [ ] **Pappy**

Have you noticed this dog? Manet has even painted his little ball! In fact, how many dogs have you spotted throughout the book?

Woman with a Fan

Modigliani

Let me introduce you to Lunia
*I'm Modi!
She's a great friend of mine. I love painting her portrait and telling her my little secrets. Look at her face. It's as pointed as her fan. It's like a sculpture. Do you want a clue for recognizing my paintings? I often forget the pupils of the eyes... Shh!*

This elongated neck deserves a beautiful necklace...
Still, she doesn't have one, though she likes jewelry. Look at her fingers! In fact, I purposely simplify everything. I stretch out the body's lines, too, which makes my drawings very geometric!

On another page,
*there is a girl who is also holding a fan.
1st clue: there's a small dog at her feet.
2nd clue: we see her from the back.
Who painted her? ....*

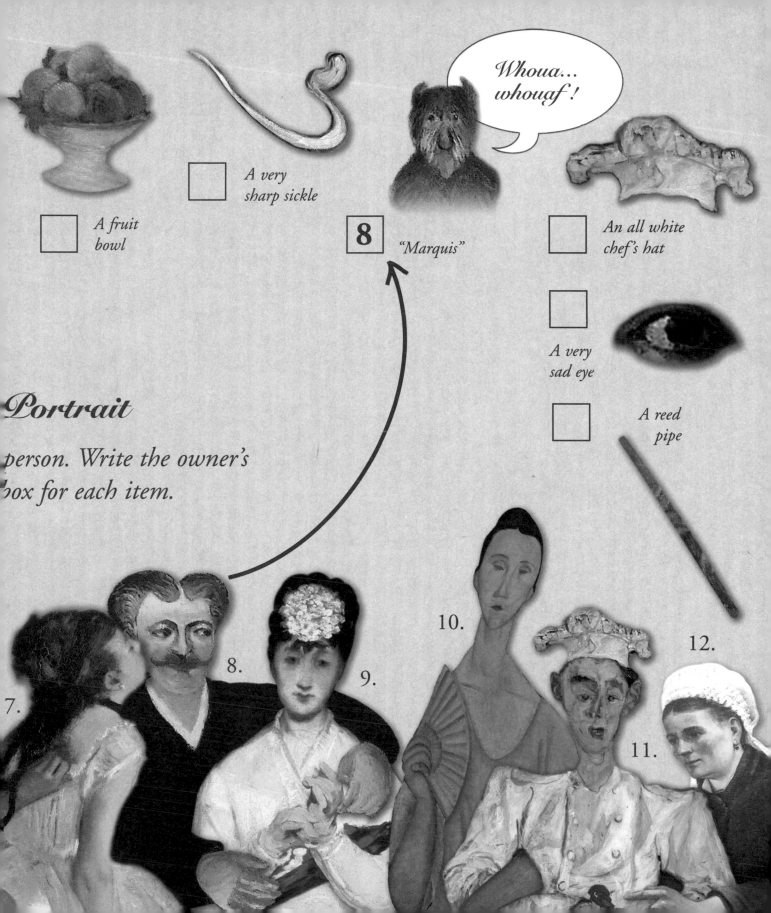

Whoua… whouaf !

☐ A fruit
bowl

☐ A very
sharp sickle

8 "Marquis"

☐ An all white
chef's hat

☐ A very
sad eye

☐ A reed
pipe

Portrait

person. Write the owner's
box for each item.

7.

8.

9.

10.

11.

12.

Rousseau

Allow me to present my friend the grocer...
His shop is next to my place. Here I've painted him surrounded by his family. And I haven't forgotten a single person...neither his dog, Marquis, nor his mare, Rosa!

And here, well, that's me!
Did you know that before becoming a painter, I worked in customs? That's why I 'm called "The Customs Officer."

From the biggest...to the smallest!
Why is his niece, dressed in white, much smaller than Junier, the father or his wife? Because I've painted them in relation to their importance. You can see this type of naïve painting on very old pictures in churches.

It looks like I took a photo here...
The figures or people are posing in front of me...while I'm in the painting! It's funny. Notice how precise each detail is. And the vivid colors make the black and white stand out.

Old Man Junier's Trap

Junier, the father, has become as famous as my painting!

The Junier family is looking for a restaurant! Have you seen on somewhere in the book? Where is it?

....

Who is this?

Do you want my glasses...?

And what would you put in the wagon?

During these years…
The Eiffel Tower was under construction; Pasteur discovered the vaccine against rabies and school became mandatory…

On the Omnibus

The top hat…quite a symbol!
He who wears it appears both taller and more elegant.
He calls for respect. The middle-class people of my time all
wore one! To make fun of it, it was also called a "stovepipe
hat." How many are there in the omnibus? ....

Delondre

No one knows my date of birth!
*I know, I'm not famous. All that is known is that
I painted this picture around 1885... That's .... years ago.*

Driver... Please!
*In your opinion, do you think that the woman on
the outside is going to sit on the hat box? True,
my painting is not very modern, but is a
"commentary"! You see both the fashion and
means of transport of my time. You know,
subways had not yet been invented!*

**This gentleman is...well,
not very discreet!**
*You see how he's looking at his neighbor? Look
at the woman who has just come back from the
market... And the one at the back who looks
exhausted. Her baby's trying to sleep, but
the horses are making too much noise!*

A "stovepipe" is

- ✂ a radiator
- ✏ a hat
- ✒ a fur coat

Riddle

I am as white as the flour
used for my cakes, who am I?

Matisse painted...

- ✂ red meat
- ✒ very red tomatoes
- ✏ red fish

Van Gogh painted his portrait with one ear cut off

✏ True   ✒ False

On the island of Tahiti, women wear...

- ✂ Swimsuits
- ✏ Traditional Tahitian dresses
- ✒ Divos

Old man Junier is seated

- ✒ on a motorbike
- ✏ in his cart
- ✂ on a bicycle

These fathers painted their son. It's up to you to match the fathers with the son!

Picasso ●   ● Jean
Manet ●   ● Paul
Monet ●   ● Léon

Vlaminck was a racing cyclist

✏ True
✒ False

What's this?

On which painting do you find these different objects?

Cézanne

All of my life I've painted apples

I love them...as does Zola, a childhood friend of mine. One day, I stood up for him at school. To thank me for defending him, he brought me a basket of apples! Later, we quarreled. He became famous for his books...so why not me with my paintings? So I decided "to conquer Paris with my apples"!

Geometry Recipe...

To paint a still-life, take one canvas. Paint some lines for the table, diamond shapes for the tiles and circles for the apples. Mix everything together. Add a pinch of perspective and your painting is ready. Careful... The apples are going to roll to the ground! No, no, the knife is there to keep them from falling.

The forger was caught red handed with this ⟨Soutine⟩ canvas! Who, according to you, painted the 4 additional items?

....

....

....

....

What do you think this boy looking at you is?

☐ A famous surgeon

☐ A baker boy

☐ A young groom

FAUX

Does this lunch look finished to you?
Think up another title:

....

My impressionist friends include:
Degas, Manet, Renoir, Bazille and Morisot. We drastically changed the way of painting in our time.

Monet

In my time, I was the talk of the town!
*I'm an impressionist. I paint my impressions
and what I feel. The word was invented when
my painting, "Impression, Sunrise" was discovered.*

Little Jean at 7... He's my son!
*It's so hot that he's playing in the shade! Did you see
the spots on the tablecloth? It's the shadows cast by
the tree's leaves. They will disappear or move on
in a short time. It's exactly what I wanted to
paint: something that doesn't last.*

2 meters high!
*On this gigantic canvas, I have
brought 3 styles of painting together.
Landscape: the garden at my house.
Still-life: choose whatever you'd like
on the table. And a portrait: Jean's!*

Who's wearing the hat?

What are you going to draw for your snack with this bowl of fruit?

Vlaminck

Funny name... I'm Flemish

Before becoming a painter, I was a mechanic, race cyclist and then a musician. I knew nothing about museums, I didn't have time for them... I've learned to paint all by myself!

I push on my tube and spread the paint

It is these pure touches of color that make the painting. Look at my canvas; do you notice the perspective and number of things on it? The street is without depth and the tree trunk is entirely flat. Matisse and I were called "wild," like wildcats! Do you think our colors are too intense? Anyway, why should everything have a name?

"The Machine" at Bougival

A real attraction
Louis XIV had this water wheel built on the Seine to supply water for the fountains at the Versailles castle. Everybody came to watch the 14 wheels turn!

It seems I said this!
"Painting is like cooking, you can't explain it. You have to experience it."

The restaurant is closed!
Would you like a piece of bread? It's up to you to find it in the book if you want to gobble it up!

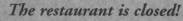

*Would you like to go out on
the terrace or in the garden?*

1.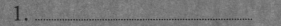

2. ....

Enqête ?
Police inquiry

ENQUÊTE

In which paintings are these items found?

3. ....

4. ....

5. ....

Clue n°1

Plouf!
You have already seen me "dressed up" 8 pages before the portrait you are looking for.

COURBET

Clue n°2

Her necklace was found... in the forger's pocket!

Once again the forger has struck!
Circle what has been changed in the three photos?

DEGAS

Le Can'art

Forger at Last Behind Bars!

Before stopping the forger, police discovered 5 paintings of young girls in his studio. One of them was painted by a woman. It was the forger's favorite painter. You have 2 clues to discover her identity. Who is she?

MORISOT

RENOIR

BAZILLE

Solutions ans... ers

The details or items that had to be found are circled on the originals and on the following page. The painter's names are written on this double page.

Things or oddities to find are:

2 couples taking a siesta: one by Coubert and the other by Van Gogh. • **There are 2 wagons:** one in Van Gogh and the other in Rousseau. • **The young awoman seen from the back** holding a fan is by Degas. • **The restaurant** is in a painting by Vlaminck. • **2 men** are wearing a top hat in the omnibus by Delondre. • **To know how old** the painting is, subtract: 2008 - 1880 = 128 years! • **The quiz:** You had to circle the changes for the right answers. • **Baker boy** is the right answer for the riddle. • **The fathers:** Picasso is Paul's father, Monet is Jean's and Leon is Manet's. Leon called him "godfather." • **The bread roll** is in a painting by Cézanne. • **The shadows:** the fan is found in Modigliani, a wheel in Rousseau, an apple and knife in Cézanne and a cow in Van Gogh.

Airplanes didn't exist yet.

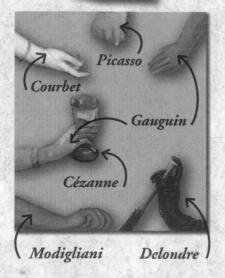

There are 6 dogs in the book.

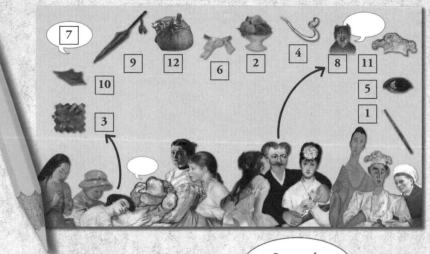

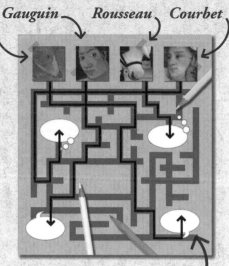

Gauguin Rousseau Courbet

And what did you write
in the bubble?

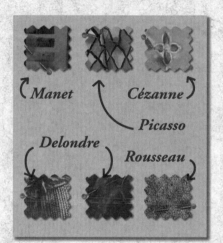

Manet   Cézanne

Picasso

Delondre   Rousseau

I am the
little baker

Rousseau

Cézanne

Manet   Matisse

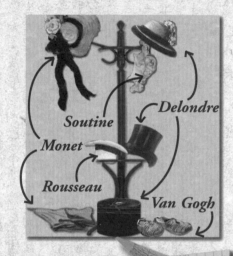

Soutine   Delondre

Monet

Rousseau   Van Gogh

**The forger's favorite
painter was Morisot**

The first clue helped you find the
gold fish by Matisse. This painting
comes 8 pages before Manet's portrait
of Berthe Morisot. She is wearing
clue n°2 around her neck.

On the 3 photos
of the girl Renoir painted, she bor-
rowed a flower from Morisot and
the cape and ribbon from Bazille.

Conception, mock-up and text:
Raphaëlle Aubert. Assistant Editor:
Laurence Cardoze. Graphic system:
Véronique Desormeaux, Katryn de Palma
and José Vilela. English translation:
D. Pereira-Egan.

© Au clair de ma plume 2008. Law n° 49-956, 16 July 1949 for publi-
cations intended for young readers. Dépôt légal: February 2008. Printed
in February 2008 at Imprimerie Desseaux & Fils / 95100 Argenteuil.

www.auclairdemaplume.com

The author wishes to thank Véronique Pellier,
Laurence Chorizo and all the proofreaders,
players and reviewers, without forgetting her
favorite little players, Cyrielle and Simon!

1800 = 19th century

1900 = 20th century

I am the oldest painting

© ADAGP, Paris 2008

© Succession H. Matisse

1857

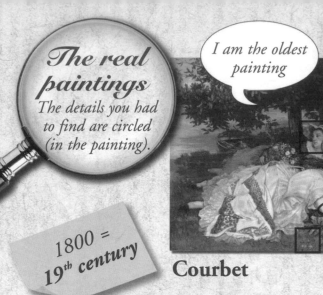

Courbet

1868

Bazille

1869

Manet

1905

Vlaminck

1893

Morisot

1892

Gauguin

1908

Rousseau

1914

Matisse

1919

Modigliani

1873

Monet

1876

Degas

1881

Cézanne

1890

Van Gogh

1888

Renoir

1885

Delondre

1923

Soutine

> And... I'm the youngest!

1924

Picasso

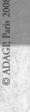

Gustave Courbet (1819-1877). *Les demoiselles du bord de la Seine*. Musée du Petit-Palais, Paris. © Photo RMN / © Bulloz. **Jean Frédéric Bazille** (1841-1870). *Vue de village*. © Photo RMN / © Droits réservés. Musée Fabre, Montpellier. **Edouard Manet** (1832-1883). *Le balcon*. Musée d'Orsay, Paris. © Photo RMN / © H. Lewandowski. **Claude Monet** (1840-1926). *Le déjeuner*. Musée d'Orsay, Paris. © Photo RMN / © H. Lewandowski. **Edgar Degas** (1834-1917). *La classe de danse*. Musée d'Orsay, Paris. © Photo RMN / © H. Lewandowski. **Paul Cézanne** (1839-1906). *Fruits, serviette et boîte à lait*. Musée de l'Orangerie, Paris. © Photo RMN / © J.-G. Berizzi. **Maurice Delondre** (19ᵉ siècle). *Dans l'omnibus*. Musée Carnavalet, Paris. © Photo Roger-Viollet. **Auguste Renoir** (1841-1919). *Jeune fille au ruban bleu*. Musée des Beaux-Arts, Lyon. © Photo RMN / © R. G. Ojéda / T. Le Mage - Musée d'Orsay, Paris. **Vincent Van Gogh** (1853-1890). *La sieste (d'après Millet)*. Musée d'Orsay, Paris. © Photo RMN / © H. Lewandowski. **Paul Gauguin** (1848-1903). *Arearea (Joyeusetés)* Musée d'Orsay, Paris. © Photo RMN / © H. Lewandowski. **Berthe Morisot** (1841-1895). *Jeune fille en décolleté*. Musée du Petit-Palais, Paris. © Photo RMN / © Bulloz. **Maurice de Vlaminck** (1876-1958). *Restaurant de la machine de Bougival*. Musée d'Orsay, Paris. © Photo RMN / © H. Lewandowski. **Henri Rousseau**, dit Le Douanier Rousseau (1844-1910). *La Carriole du Père Junier* - Musée de l'Orangerie, Paris. Coll. J. Walter et P. Guillaume. © Photo RMN / © H. Lewandowski. **Henri Matisse** (1869-1954). *Intérieur, bocal de poissons rouges*. Centre Georges Pompidou, Paris. © Photo CNAC/MNAM Dist. RMN / © J.-C. Planchet. **Amedeo Modigliani** (1884-1920). *Femme à l'éventail (Lunia Czechowska)*. Musée d'Art moderne de la Ville de Paris, Paris. © Photo RMN / © Bulloz. **Pablo Picasso** (1881-1973). *Paul en arlequin*. Musée Picasso, Paris. © Photo RMN / © J.-G. Berizzi. **Chaim Soutine** (1893-1943). *Le petit pâtissier*. Musée de l'Orangerie, Paris. Coll. J. Walter et P. Guillaume. © Photo RMN / © T. Le Mage. **J.-F. Millet** (1814-1875). *Moissonneuse endormie*. © Photo RMN / © T. Le Mage.